All the Heroes are Dead

"All the Heroes are Dead;

The Ecology of
John Steinbeck's Cannery Row "

text and photographs by

Tom Weber

Ramparts Press
San Francisco

Published by Ramparts Press, Inc.

Library of Congress Catalog Card No. 73-90633
ISBN 0-87867-052-1   (cloth)
ISBN 0-87867-053-X   (paperback)

Printed in the United States of America.

This book is for
Renate
and
Maurice Silver

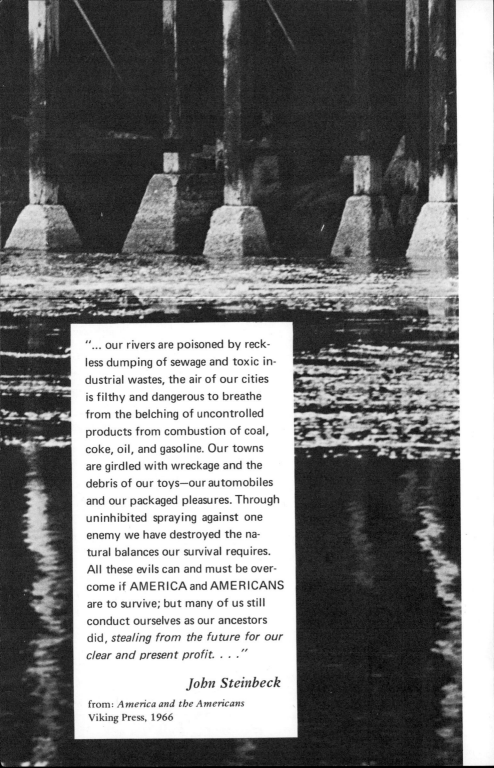

"... our rivers are poisoned by reckless dumping of sewage and toxic industrial wastes, the air of our cities is filthy and dangerous to breathe from the belching of uncontrolled products from combustion of coal, coke, oil, and gasoline. Our towns are girdled with wreckage and the debris of our toys—our automobiles and our packaged pleasures. Through uninhibited spraying against one enemy we have destroyed the natural balances our survival requires. All these evils can and must be overcome if AMERICA and AMERICANS are to survive; but many of us still conduct ourselves as our ancestors did, *stealing from the future for our clear and present profit. . . .*"

John Steinbeck

from: *America and the Americans*
Viking Press, 1966

FOREWORD

FOR TWENTY-FIVE years I watched the decline, death, and "rebirth" of Cannery Row. While my camera made frequent notes, it never occurred to me to write about the "street." Steinbeck did that before. Stories about whores and winos (bank-thieves, sex-killers, get-rich-quickers, and long-life tonics) are more palatable to the American taste than cold statistics.

During my stay on the Row, I traveled around the globe several times taking pictures and making notes for a photographic essay on the 'children of man.' A few years back in a small fishing village in southern Italy an old fisherman held my arm tightly and asked my translator if it were true that there were so many sardines off the California coast that a man could walk across them like a bridge.

I told my translator to tell the old man that all the sardines had been fished out. He released his grip and became sad. "They are getting harder to catch here, too," he said.

In Lisbon, Portugal, an old fisherwoman damned the boats in the bay and apologized to a customer because the fish were oily.

I stood on the banks of the Rhine river in Germany and watched the dead fish floating down water in a mesh of scum.

I saw the sunset over Tokyo Bay reflected in pools of industrial waste.

I saw sick seals washed ashore on Monterey Bay.

And the dead sea is dead.

In Paris I saw 12-year-old girls selling themselves in the night alleys to buy a piece of bread.

In the Philippines I knew men who worked all day to buy one small fish and saved the head for tomorrow.

"Cannery Row," Japan

An Indian beggar in Calcutta offered to pierce his arm with a knife for a coin to buy rice.

In Istanbul, hunger made men too deaf to hear a call to prayer.

Returning to Monterey after my last European tour, I found myself spending more and more time walking through the old barns on Cannery Row and talking to the few remaining old fishermen.

Their big regret, they said, was the loss of the fish. Many of them saved their boats for their sons. But when the sons grew up, the fish were gone and they took construction jobs or opened small stores.

"Lumber's going the way the fish did," one young man told me. "Costs too much to build. I'll have to find another job."

His cousin who owns a small grocery store is selling out. "I'm tired beating my head against the wall of the big supermarket. Small grocer can't survive with food shortage and high prices. Day of the small man is finished."

The son of one of the wealthy fishing families is spending the family fortune developing waterfront land into commercial property. "That's called conversion," he said. "You can be damn sure I'm going to leave my kid a few bucks."

"Perhaps it would have been better to leave him a few fish," I said.

"Fish be damned," he said. "Money talks."

"One day it'll lose its voice," I said.

"You're nuts," he said. "Money's here forever."

"What will be left to buy?"

Needs of the people are the same the world over: food for hunger, water for thirst, a bed to sleep upon, and clean air to sustain life; a fertile land that yields a crop and a living sea with living things.

I recalled the places I traveled and the things I saw as I wandered through the cannery shells. There was something sad

"Cannery Row," Portugal

about the old buildings that reminded me of worked-out mine shafts, forgotten barn frames on eroded soil, and barren mountain-heads shorn of their trees.

Cannery Row, drunk with the "glory" of the past, is limping through the present with Steinbeck as a cane—and uncertain of the future.

I find a universal quality in the frantic, fearful, grasping character of the Row that reminds me of streets I walked on in every major nation of the world. There is thoughtless depletion of the sea and earth, followed by mad land booms with little concern for the needs of man.

I talked with an old prostitute who worked on Cannery Row for Flora Wood. In a passing comment, she said:

> "Nowadays you got all them fine people who
> call themselves clean and they're messin' up
> the world till a soul could die of the stink..."

Perhaps there is a story here that is worth the telling.

Tom Weber

Monterey, California

"Cannery Row," the Philippines

CONTENTS

INVOCATION

WHO is to say an automaker,
     smog-spiller,
     earth-killer,
paper-maker,
rock-blaster,
meat-butcher,
steel-smelter,
fish-canner,
          have less a dream than God?

"You can not live without us," they say.
"Nor long with you," comes back
     the ghost-word in a sheath of silence.

Famine lies quiet
     in the waters of the world.
It cannot be heard like the cry of a hungry child.

But that does not make it
   less a famine.
One day it will rise like a cloud,
   break the crust of soiled water
   and drench the earth in hunger.

When mines run dry
   and forest stumps
   are tombstones for trees,
   when the last lonely caribou
   becomes a pair of leather shoes
   and a sparrow looks vainly
   for flower seed
   on dead soil;
   when winds of sand
   cover the land
   and green lake slime
   snares the last fisher-crane,
   who will be left to say
   man had a lesser dream than God?

Man pours pollution into the sea . . .
and sheds a tear for a seal he killed
with man-made poison.

CANNERY ROW,
    hurrah and farewell!
    Dying mother in a glittering shroud
of *progress,*
pallor of death
warmed by carnival lights,
funeral dirge of copper quarters
and tourist dimes,
washed by new tides of polluted water
and dead seal;
mirror of the world—
built on the bones of yesterday's "forever."

There were none before
    but the giant bison
    and sabertooth tiger,
    the monster wolf
    and the condor . . .

The lonely hunter could find food without poison.

growing strong and becoming many,
   wandering over "Cannery Row."
They breathed a wind
   scented only by the seasons,
   good air touched only by the breath
   of flowering trees.

There was no "taking" then,
   only a "giving,"
   earth giving to the
   tree and tree giving to the earth,
   with clear water wetting the
   membrane of life.
Rains that fell were pure
   and the air didn't beg for cleaning.
The only song was quiet,
   the only tears were rain.
Shall we say this came first?

But First is never last.

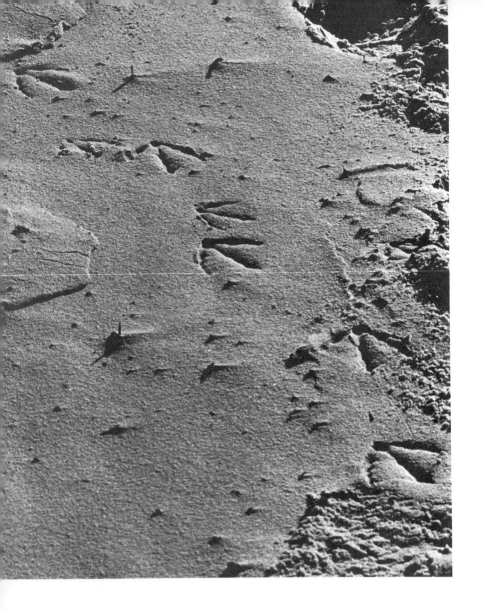

Tracks of beast and bird grow fewer,
swallowed by the quicksands of "progress."

ANCIENT MAN stumbled
along the Monterey coast,
much the same as he did along
all coasts, much the same
as he did over the shore line
of every sea and river.
Was that twenty thousand years ago?
Little difference between twenty thousand
and ten.
Time is only important
when there is pending death.
Earth wasn't dying then.

Ancient man came,
dislodging a stone only to survive,
taking water where he found it,
never changing the course of a river;
loving the soil as a brother,
water as a son,

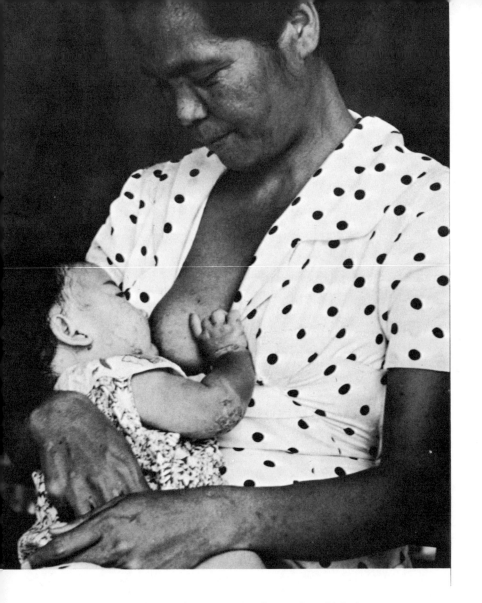

Hunger—disease—poison . . . the fountain of birth
we thought would flow forever, carries the taste of
death . . .

sky as an ancestor,
neither knowing where he came from
nor where he was.
Like the other animals,
he lay down with a female
and she bore him a child.
She suckled her young
like the wolf and the tiger,
one with the earth,
one with wind, rain, and sun,
one with all seasons,
son of a fertile mother,
daughter of a fertile sire.
Ancient man came second.

But Second is never last.

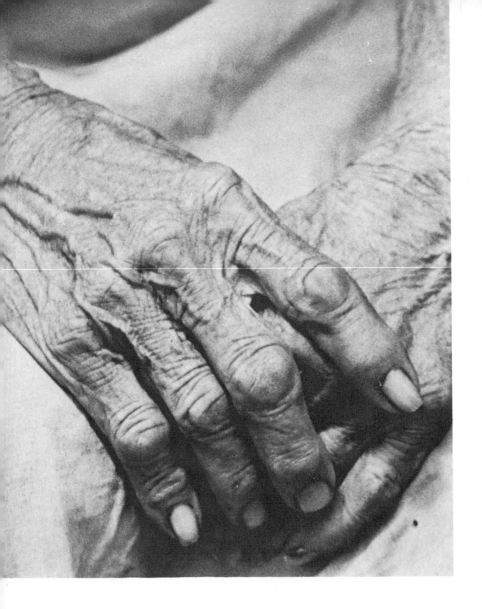

The Indian thought of his hands as the boughs of a tree
. . . given to him by his Gods to shelter the lives of his
children.

ANCIENT MAN lay down with his woman.
They embraced each other
for thousands of years
and he warmed her womb with Indian sperm,
and splashed the shores of "Monterey"
with sons and sons of daughters.

To read some history,
    one would think
    the Indian was born of an evil wind;
    his only "evil" was living,
    her only "evil," helping him.
They lived together in the coastal forest
    of Monterey.
He fished off a beach
    in living water and dried his
    fish on "Cannery Row;"
    collected shells to trade for pelts
    to warm his body
    and cover his child.

We "honor" the Indian by selling his artifacts
for high prices
and hanging his picture on rusty sardine boilers.

The fog was just as chilling then.
He moved among the plants
   in a rustling whisper,
   stalked the deer but called the deer
   his brother,
   milled his meal
   from buckeye and acorns,
   mixed the mush with berries and meat;
   there were always pine nuts
   to finish the hunger.

What tribes were these, you ask.
Call them Costanoan, Salinan, Esselen,
   first call them gentle.
They chanted their songs
   and the seasons gave them words;
   a prayer to the sky for rain,
   a prayer to the earth for abundance;
   rain came,
   earth unfolded each harvest,
   earth and sea were bountiful.
They treated their food
   with love,
   said it had a spirit,
   that it was born, grew,
   and served its birthright
   by nurturing other life
   and returning to the ground
   to nourish new seed.
They lived in small huts
   made from willow and tule;
   to hold the fruits of the earth,

It is written on the clouds of a stormy sky that the earth
will avenge herself, and strike down her killers!
The innocent will suffer, too.

they made baskets from roots and grass.
But they only took enough.
These were the "savages"
   who walked on "Cannery Row" . . .
   sharing a common heart
   with brothers
   on other shores.

What tribes were these, you ask.
Costanoan, Salinan, Esselen,
   brothers of the Blackfoot and Sioux,
   the Chippewa and Apaches,
   cousins of the Seneca and Creek,
   tied to their brothers and cousins
   by deep reverence for the living.
While their tongues were different,
   they sat on the same earth.
Words of their songs
   were the same.

Their women were root diggers,
   mush makers, and basket weavers.
They dried the fish
   and gathered grass seed,
   leached the acorn,
   and opened their loins
   to flower the earth with a crop of people.
Her man was a hunter of food,
   a trapper of game,
   catcher of fish.
But he never forgot
   that earth was the source of all life.

LOOSED UPON J

U.S. Puts "Most Terrible Destructive Force in History" to Military Use

Single Bomb Carries More Power Than 20,000 Tons of TNT; Tokyo Told New Weapon Is Answer to Failure to Quit

WASHINGTON, Aug. 6 (A)—An atomic bomb, hailed as the most terribly destructive force in history and as the greatest achievement of organized science, has been loosed upon Japan.

President Truman disclosed in a White House statement today that the first use of the bomb—containing more power than 20,000 tons of TNT and producing more than 2,000 times the blast of the most powerful bomb ever dropped before—was made 16 hours earlier on Hiro Shima, Japanese army base.

The atomic bomb ... answer, President Truman said, to Japan's refusal to surrender Secretary of W... predicted the bomb will "prove a tremendous aid" in shortening the Japanes...

IMPENF'...
Mr ...

CLOAKS FIRST TARGET
...arned that "eve... powerful forms (of the bomb) are in de-

accept our ter'... xpect a rain of ruin from the air the
r been seen on
...nt reported that cloud of dust and smoke" cloaked
ne first atomic bomb was impossible to make an im-
mediate as...
damage.

Germans Were Searching for Secret Too

SECRET GUARDED
President Truman said ...
recommend that congress co...
...stablishing a commission to con-
trol production of atomic power
within the United States, adding:

Sidelights 'n New U.S. Super-weapon

The Indian used his arrow to gather meat and pelts for his children. White man called it a "savage" weapon. "Civilized man" has come a long way in a hundred years.

He had neither fear of death
  nor hunger for life.
He lived his days
  like the rabbit in the field
  and the fish in the sea,
  took each waking moment as he went
  until he met the evening sky.

One day,
  without warning,
  white plague
  swept over the Indians on "Cannery Row,"
  moved like a crazy quilt over
  all the Indians of all the land.
The plague made the good earth "sore."

An old Wintu Indian woman
  said it better:
"When we Indians kill meat,
  we eat it all up.
When we dig roots, we make little holes.
When we build houses,
  we make little holes.
When we burn grass for grasshoppers,
  we don't ruin things.
We shake down acorns and pinenuts,
We don't chop down the tree.
We only use dead wood.
But white people plough up the ground,
  pull down trees,
  ruin everything."

As man's hunger for power and wealth gets greater, so do his land-shattering monsters that "make the earth sore."

The tree says, "Don't, I am sore.
Don't hurt me!"
But they chop it down and cut it up.
The spirit of the land
   hates the white man.
They blast out trees
   and stir up
   the mother earth.
They saw up the trees
That hurts them.
Indians never hurt anything.
But white people destroy all.
They blast rocks and scatter them
   on the ground.
The rock says:
"Don't, you are hurting me."
But white people pay no attention.
When the Indians use rocks,
   they take little round ones
   for cooking.
How can the spirit of the earth
   like the white man?
Everywhere the white man has touched,
   it is sore . . ."

The Indian and his ancestor
   lived on "Cannery Row"
for twenty thousand years.
The Indian was third.

But Third is never last.

Christ is my anchor, the Spaniard said. But he always
carried a couple spares, along with an arsenal
and holy water to bless his weapons.

TWO HUNDRED years ago
the Spaniards came to "Cannery Row,"
came with the word of God
and Christianity
for the "pagan" Indian
who destroyed no man,
wanted no gold,
needed only shells for his neck;
sang stories of beauty,
told stories of strength,
revered his father
and thanked the fertile bay
for its harvest of silver fish.
Always in the name of Christ
the Spaniard came,
always with the crucifix for a spear,
maps of fabled cities of gold
in his hand.

Most missions were built by the Indians. The Padres
nailed up iron gates to keep God in . . . and the
Indians out.

He doused the Indian fire
    with holy water
    and made the Indian squaw
    sick with syphilis.
The Spaniard came
    looking for gold,
    for land,
    for a seaport
    to harbor his ships
    for the Manila trade.
Looking for everything but God.
He had plenty of
God.
His God came well packaged
    in "Padre cloth."
The Spaniard taught the Indian
    the word of God with the point
    of his God-annointed saber.
The Spaniard praised the Lord
    and stole the Indian's furs
    and hides and land
    and women.
He corralled the Monterey Indians
    like cattle and drove them
    into the missions.
Taught them modesty
    and shame of their naked bodies,
    made the women cover their breasts
    and their loins.
In the night,
    the Spaniard raped the Indian women,
    to teach her the ways

A new mission wall built for the tourist camera and privately paid for with hope the donor can "buy" special rewards from God.

of God fearing men.

Indian tongues
    were "pagan" tongues and the Padres
    taught the Indian Spanish,
    spoke to him of brotherhood
    and sacrifice for God.
Especially *sacrifice.*
The Padres could never
    understand how the Indian survived
    without knowing how to
    shoe a horse, tan a hide,
    raise a crop, or make a wagon,
    weave more cloth than he ever needed,
    hunt more food than he ever could eat,
    trap more skins than he ever wanted.
"Untamed savage," the Padres said,
    mistaking humility for stupor,
    calling the docile Indian a coward.
"Enslave the Indian
    for his own good," the Spaniard said,
    "teach him the ways of civilization."
And just to get off on the right foot,
    the Padres showed the Indian
    how to build missions
    or perhaps the better word
    is "rebuild" missions,
    for it is well recorded
    that the Padres were
    thieves for God.
One sect trying to outdo another,

ANCHOR
FROM THE
MONTEREY
1944
TOWN

The old custom house plaza is a place of meeting for
old fishermen. This one said, "They're fishing out
sardines so small in Italy, you can pick your teeth
with them . . ."

stole whole missions, piece by piece,
and on the backs of the Indians,
transplanted the missions
to a farther outpost,
leaving the plundered missionaries
sitting helplessly in the wilderness,
until they too, became plunderers.
Ways of the white skin's God
    are strange
    thought the Indians
    and they wanted to hide in the forests.
Some stayed through fear,
    others were killed.
Those who ran were already dead,
    for they were separated forever
    from the soil of their ancestors.

Yes, the Spaniard carried the wisdom
    of the Lord and used the wisdom
    to built a customs house
    in Monterey,
    for wisdom is getting rich
    and getting rich was the Spaniards'
    highest tribute to the Lord.
Every trading vessel
    passing through Monterey
    received a word of God from a Padre
    and it was welcome to drop anchor
    . . . after it paid high duty
    on its cargo
    and carried a ship's license
    blessed by the Spanish

Casa Vasquez.
Originally a one-story
adobe. Former home of the
sister of Tiburcio Vasquez,
Monterey's colorful bandit.

Monterey History & Art Assn.

We preach honesty to our children and glorify our criminals. We jail one man for poaching a salmon and hail as a "hero" another who steals the ocean empty.

and properly taxed
   to buy more holy water.
The Spaniard
   taxed the cargo ship
   from Boston and China,
   taxed the whaling ships
   from New England.
Sold ship supplies
   at high prices,
   levied fines,
   and demanded tribute.
Praise the Lord!
The Spaniards got rich
   and left nice homes
   around Cannery Row.
California preserves them
   as a tribute to
   the Spaniard's
   "contribution" to civilization.
The Spaniard came fourth.

But Fourth is never last.

The "pioneer" came with his pots and pans, his booze and gun. He came as an evangelist for freedom, preacher of honesty. He enslaved the docile and took his spoils.

THE PIONEERS came,
   sagebrushers and desert rats,
   bunchgrassers and sandcutters,
  sheepherders and prairie dogs.
Their nicknames were many,
  their goal, the same:
"Strike it rich."
These stalwarts of "new" America
  hailed equality
  and counted the Indian scalps
  in their saddle bags;
  struck a hard blow for democracy,
  and the blow was fatal to many.
The first pioneers
  came on horseback,
  by foot,
  overland,
  by sea.

With every rotation of the wagon wheel, the "pioneer" took a little more Indian earth. He was *not* a hero in his conquest of the West. He was forced to defend the things he stole. His accomplices were the federal troops.

The pioneer mingled with the Spaniard
   and the Spaniard
   mingled with pioneer
   and the pioneer
   with his Yankee know-how
   taught the Spaniard a thing or two.
The pioneer praised the Lord
   for such a bountiful land . . .
And took it away from the Spaniard.

The first pioneer
   was a horse-trader,
   claim-jumper,
   Indian-hater,
   gambling shark,
   gun-dealer.
He was also
   a carpenter,
   mason,
   baker,
   farmer,
   story-teller,
   song-singer.
He fancied himself
   fierce and cunning,
   fearless and gallant,
   chivalrous and intrepid.
He told stories about himself
   and praised himself
   in song,
   sang about his conquests:
   Indians he scalped,

. . . the barber deserted his chair, joined the gold rush and let his hair grow long.

mountains he climbed,
famine he survived,
buffalo he killed,
poker games he won,
women he loved,
trees he felled,
rocks he moved,
and storms he lived through.
He thrived on his own stories of cunning,
believed his own stories of ferocity,
and like all pioneers of all time
in all places,
whistled to keep his courage up.
He wanted to be more than he was,
own more than he needed,
win for the sake of winning,
eat for the sake of eating,
build for the sake of building;
birds that flew were for his killing,
earth was for his keeping,
seas were for his plundering
much the same as the pioneers
before him . . .
and those who came after.

He tilled the wrong soil in the
wrong place for the wrong crop,
chopped down forests
and made cracks in the earth,
massacred buffalo for hides
and let famine swallow
the Indian nations.

... the farmer who killed the Indian and conquered the
West for the love of his plough, turned his fickle love
to the metal, gold.

Most of all, he was broke.
The California gold rush
   made him forget
   who he was,
   where he was,
   what he was
   and why he came to Monterey.
He sold his hammer,
   his trowel,
   his plough,
   his home,
   his woman,
   abandoned his boat,
   deserted the army,
   and headed north
   where the rush was on.
The pioneer came fifth.

But Fifth is never last.

. . . the drayman was stricken with gold fever, too, and left what he thought he wanted most—for the dream of "more."

WHILE the pioneer
was panning for gold,
playing poker,
singing a "brag" song,
drinking his whiskey,
spending his dust
on a mine camp whore . . .
a dyed in the wool "heathen"
laid down to rest on "Cannery Row."
You could tell right off
he was a "heathen" . . .
skin was "yaller,"
didn't have that healthy tone
of a good white Yankee.
Eyes were "crooked."
"A critter thet can't
look yer straight in th' eye,
ain't no better'n a
varmint."

There are still remnants of the gold rush days—
mounds of rock torn from the ground, and rusting
relics of grasping "heroes."

His God had another name
   and he came from a far country
   called China.
"Never heerd of it, but wherever
   in tarnation it lays, it can't
   come up t' the ass
   ov this good earth...!''

When the Chinese lay down
   on "Cannery Row," it was because
   they were tired and hungry
   after walking down from the gold
   country where they were
   chased by the pioneers who
   just walked up there from "Cannery Row."
The pioneers were tired
   from their walk, too.
After they rested up a little
   they went out
   to find themselves a claim—
They found the "heathen."
So they went back to town
   and slubbered
   some more rot gut whiskey,
   played a hand of poker,
   "felt-up" a mine camp whore
   and held a meeting.

Them "Yaller heathens"
   don't look like white men,
   don't smell like white men,
   don't wear the same clothes as white men,

43

In the new spirit of the American Bill of Rights,
the miners burned down the "heathen" temple.

don't believe in the white man's God;
   must come from the devil.
They had to go!
Besides, the industrious Chinese
   who got there first
   had staked the richest claims.
So the pioneers shot the hell
   out of the Chinese,
   lassoed them, cut off their pigtails,
   burned their temples, fired their camp.
But saved one for a cook.
So you can understand
   why the Chinese were tired when they
   arrived on "Cannery Row."
They cooked seaweed,
   ate dried fish,
   lay down to rest,
   dreamed of their Yangtze river homes
   and moved
   their village to "Cannery Row"
   when they awoke.
Their junk-timber shacks
   reached out over Monterey Bay,
   one foot on land,
   the other in the water
   as though they were holding earth and sea together,
   just as the Yangtze river shacks
   hold earth and river together.

The Chinese
   feared no work,
   asked no favor,

The Chinese were happy in their fishing shacks. They figured with the "sons of freedom" chasing wealth in the gold fields, they would have some peace on "Cannery Row."

made no threat.
He was happy.
He found seaweed and crabs,
    mussels and squid,
    abalone and oysters.
Fish and descendants of fish,
    perch and flounder
    cod and mackerel,
    rockfish and blue fish,
    yellow tail and sand dabs
    and most of all—salmon.

They were all living
    their natural fish lives,
    making love,
    eating plankton,
    and chasing around,
    fat and strong and confident
    their progeny would be
    swimming the shoals of "Cannery Row"
    for another 20 thousand years.
That was 140 years ago
    when there were so many ducks,
    they blotted out the sun.
To walk in the forest
    was to frighten a deer.
Wild berry bushes grew on "Cannery Row"
    with none to do the taking,
    but a bird who ate the berry
    and dropped the seed
    to plant another berry bush.
The sea wasn't dying then.

The Indians and Chinese took a few abalone, but the shellfish didn't mind. They could keep up with the moderate demand . . .

Back in those days
    when the Chinese gentlemen and their ladies
    caught their catch,
    dried the squid,
    cleaned the fish,
    and gutted the abalone,
    all the world was feeling "okay."
The sea wasn't hurting
    and the earth wasn't "sore" . . .
Everyone was happy
    because there were heaps to take,
    and those who could, took a heap.

Miners ransacked the earth
    for the last pinch of pay-dirt.
Mine camp whores married claim jumpers
    and carted their fortunes . . .
    to San Francisco
    to set up banks;
    bought land,
    built big homes, sported fancy rags
    and became codfish aristocracy.
Their "cousins" hung around
    Monterey and Pacific Grove
    keeping an eye on the "heathen"
    and his "strange carryin's on."

After dark, when good Christians
    were doing what good Christians do,
    the man from China
    pushed himself out to bay
    in a homemade sampan

The sea otter was an interested spectator. He really didn't care what anyone did, so long as they left him a few abalone. Today he is being threatened.

with a basket in the bow.
He built a fire in the basket
   and dropped his nets
   to catch the fish that came
   to see a "heathen's" fire.
Man and woman
   worked together,
   manned the boat,
   netted the fish
   and "pampered" them
   when they were dead.

"Well, Lord, t' see that
   wild carryin on at night.
They'd get out there in them devil boats
   with baskets ov livin' fire in them
   an' how they would scream an' shout
   an' beat the poor ocean
   jes' t' scare th' livin' daylights
   outta them fish till they ran int'
   the heathen's net and was dern glad
   t' call it quits.
"Why a soul could hardly
   get near them Chinamen shacks
   with th' stink an' sech.
All them squids hangin' in th' sun
   an' all them Chinamens working right on
   like they was breathin' honeysuckle.
"Am willin' to say they didn't sleep none
   with fishin' all night
   an pamperin' them dead fish
   all day."

There were many kinds of fish to fish out . . .
Today the fish population is way down and
many species carry a variety of poisons: mercury,
toxic crop sprays.

While the "Chinamens" were getting born,
   dying off,
   getting born again and shipping
   fish to San Francisco and China,
   turning squid into fertilizer,
   polishing abalone shells . . .
   the white cousins in Monterey
   were circling to the left,
   circling to the right,
   clapping their hands,
   beating their chests,
   begging the good Lord to lead them
   to the golden glory road.

Then it was that the Lord opened their eyes.
It was right there in front of them:
   the whole world was a reservoir
   of "never ending" things that would
   go on and on and . . .
   railroads to build,
   lands to milk sterile;
   banks to open,
   homes to loan on,
   forests to empty,
   fish to fish out,
   stores for dry goods,
   old goods, any goods,
   land to buy, buy it cheap,
   "it don't need no ice to keep.
Hold it forty, sixty years,
   make your folks all millionaires."

The earth was a treasure house of good things that could net a man a tidy profit, like coal and iron and oil and—

Folks will blow it in a day,
    blow the whole damn world away.
Now that ain't natural thinkin'
    for a good white American gentleman.
Where's that pioneer spirit?
Get yourself out there, boy, and cut
    yourself a piece of God's green earth.
If the earth's all gone,
    grab yourself a piece of the ocean.
Get out there and cross and doublecross,
    buy low, sell high.
Be happy when you strike it rich.
The founding fathers
    say it's your constitutional right;
    you got lots of liberty,
    "just don't get caught with your pants down."

That was how all the
    "Cannery Rows" were gobbled up.
All in the name of:
    long live Jefferson
    with the pursuit of anything
    you can get away with
    if some other guy doesn't punch
    you in the nose
    and even then it doesn't matter
    if you have a recorded deed
    because that makes it yours.
"Hear me now," the lawyer said,
    "and if justice prevails, we'll appeal."

Some of the mining cousins

The last reminder of Chinese fishermen on Cannery Row
is a fading mural on a condemned hotel.

didn't strike it so rich
because the Mother Lode's
tits ran dry.
They came drifting back
to Cannery Row,
sometimes taking a year or ten,
the Irish,
Italians,
Portuguese,
Spaniards,
Norwegians,
Swedes,
speculators
and bonanza hunters.

But there were bad times.
Grain-crop farmers
were drowned out by rain
and salted down in
drought-dust;
jobs were tough to get and
sure as hell it was the
fault of the "Chinamen."

The Chinese
made the depression,
brought the rain,
followed it with drought,
polluted the air,
took away the white man's job,
and generally did everything
that every other minority group

Southern Pacific's iron horse that rolled slipshod over land and people is a rusting epitaph to the "Rights of Man."

did at one time or another
on other Cannery Rows
around these great
United States.
And besides, they committed
an unforgivable sin
against democracy
by getting in the way of
a railroad.

Southern Pacific Railroad
carved itself a prime cut
of Monterey coast land
and it tasted so good,
they wanted all of it.
The Chinese fishing village
was in the way.
The Chinese were sixth.

But Sixth is never last.

Men like these, poor men, young men, proud men,
took over "Cannery Row," hitched their boat to a
dream and thought the fish would go on forever.

A NEW BREED of man
stood on Cannery Row,
waved his hands,
screamed into the wind,
cursed the yellow man
for brutality against the fish,
studied his strange trawl boat,
envied his catch,
damned the Chinese fishing village
and stood in judgment
of the yellow man. . . .
Besides, Southern Pacific Railroad
couldn't stand the stink
of drying fish
and
they wanted the land
where the Chinese slept.
"They're ruining the land," SP said.

e Daily Review

PACIFIC GROVE, CAL. THURSDAY. MAY 17, 1906

PICTURESQUE CHINATOWN ONLY A MEMORY

Fire Ends a Long Controversy

Looting adds to the Losses Sustained by the Chinese

Shortly before 8 o'clock on Wednesday evening fire broke out in a barn in the west end of Chinatown, which resulted in the almost total destruction of that much discussed piscatorial settlement. Out of about fifty buildidngs, sheds and backs only nineteen remain: twelve at the west end of the village, four at the east end, and the joss house and three small huts south of the railroadtrack.

As soon as possible after the discovery of the fire, word was sent to this city and the volunteer fire department at once responded to the call. Before they could reach the scene, however, the flames had gained

fences to safety and all the usual ludicrous and pathetic incidents of a fire were enacted. One Chinese woman was seen to carry load after load of struggling chickens and geese to a place of security and then return to dash buckets of water on a burning bit of worthless fence. Most of the Celestials however treated the matter with the traditional Oriental calm as a stroke of Fate and made little or no effort to stop the spread of the flames. To the spectators, this calmness and non-activity seemed preferable to the frenzied efforts, dangerous to life and limb, which were made by the volunteer firemen amid the smoke and intense heat of

commanding a view of the scene were dotted with spectators, most of whom did not depart until the fire had burnt itself out. As a glorious and fearful spectacle this fire holds the record for this vicinity.

In contrast to the determined and heroic work of the fire fighters, one feature stands out in shameful relief: the looting indulged in by men and boys during the progress of the fire. Stores and dwellings were entered in the confusion, and articles of all kinds freely taken; some things were stolen even after they had been removed to a supposedly safe place. Officer Fred Tennant of Pacific Grove and Martin Birks of Montaney

"They're stinking up the air,"
   the good Christians said.
"They're making too much money,"
   the new breed of man said.
So the SP and the good Christians
   and the new breed of man
   crawled into one bed
   and the love affair got so hot,
   it burned down
   the Chinese fishing village.

"T' hear them people say it,
   you'd think it was the
   second coming of Christ.
You'd think God hit them
   heathens with a lightning bolt,
   punishing them infidels
   for worshipping wooden gods.
But it was the work of man,
   sure as there's a fish left in the sea.
My papa told me
   that a fisherman friend told him
   that a police officer told him
   that a fireman told him
   just how them 'Chinamen'
   shacks come to be burned down.
A couple white boys
   was hired to set fire
   in one of them shacks,
   then call the firemen.
When that old fire truck
   answered the alarm,

On the ashes of the Chinese fishing shacks, the new "Pioneers" built "modern" canneries like these.

they revved up the engine,
    hitched up the hose
    and before you know'd it,
    somebody went and axed that hose
    right through and the water
    just washed down the street.
Then somebody started
    a bucket brigade, and the more they
    passed them buckets,
    the hotter the fire got.
Seems like somebody was mixing
    kerosene with the water,
    and them poor yellow devils
    was burned out of house and home.
There was great rejoicing
    in Monterey and Pacific Grove
    because the good folks figured
    they fried two fish in one pan,
    got rid of the "heathens"
    and put an end to the stink
    of drying fish.
But the only thing that fire did
    was clear the land
    for them that wanted it,
    and the stink got worse."

Southern Pacific's little brother,
    Pacific Improvement Company
    fenced off the burned-down
    remains of Chinatown,
    warned "trespassers"
    they were on the wrong side of God,

e Daily Review

PACIFIC GROVE, CAL. TUESDAY, MAY 22, 1906

CHINESE PUT UP FIGHT AND WAR IS NOW ON

Arrests Have Been Made on Both Sides

And Litigation May Result and Continue for Years

Pacific Grove or the P. I. [...] [illegible body text]

Fund Being Raised for Destitute Chinese

The courts struck a blow for "justice." Arrests were made on "both sides"! The Chinese were jailed and fined. The men who burned down their homes were released.

posted armed guards
    to give the Almighty a little help.
The Chinese ignored the
    gun-waving sons of "justice"
    and sashayed right in and
    lay down in the ashes
    of their homes.
(Wasn't much left after
    the looters finished.)

There are ways to bring
    a man to the floor before his peers,
    call the police,
    call the army,
    call the national guard;
    call him a "yellow-heeled nester,
    ground hog,
    greasy-sacker;
    call him "heathen."
Starve him to death,
    threaten his wife,
    turn off the water.
Hit him on the head when he isn't looking.

The Chinese moved away.
Hurrah for progress,
    said the real estate men,
    we'll raise the price of lots.
Hurrah for progress said
    the new breed of man,
    I'm now protector
    of the blue bay and silver fish.

The seal was getting nervous. Until man came with his new gear, it didn't have to worry about getting shot in the head for accidentally swimming into a net.

"Long live the fish," he hollered.
He hollered so loud
    they heard him in fishing villages
    around the world.
And the fishermen came to "Cannery Row"
    to help "save" the silver fish
    because the fish in their own backyards
    were getting too thin
    to take care of the appetites
    of Italians, Spaniards,
    Greeks, Portuguese,
    Swedes and
    whoever else eats fish.
They brought all kinds of fancy rigs
    and pulleys,
    clubs and hooks
    to "preserve" the fish.
The new breed
    looked through the smoke
    in Chinatown
    and screamed:
    "Burn it all down,
    but, for Christ's sake
    save the fishing gear
    so we can find out
    how they caught fish."
(No more than a couple hundred
    pounds a day, as the records show it.)
But that up-and-coming
    new breed used the "ol' noodle,"
    copied a little here,
    stole a little there,

69

Man didn't like the drabness of clean beaches so he added
a little color, variety, and interest to the ocean kelp.

borrowed when he could,
threw in a twist of the screw
and sent it to Washington
for a patent . . .
even though it might have been used
two thousand years ago in China.

"Them yellow-heels' rigs didn't
    catch many damn fish any nohow,
    but two hundred pounds
    is two hundred pounds.
Let's get to the paydirt!"
The new hungry fishermen
    rowed around Monterey Bay
    in their little dinghies
    and when they looked down in the
    clear bay water
    and saw the sardines and salmon
    swimming in silver rivers,
    they got the same hungry feeling they had,
    when they walked into a whore house
    and looked at the girls.
Pull out the cork
    and let the water run out.
"Let's eat it all up!"
But a man's dream
    is always a little ahead
    of his pocketbook and the times,
    so the pisanos (and whatever the brotherly
    word is for Portuguese and Spaniards
    and Scandanavians)
    slopped around the bay

Man is depleting the ocean of salmon.
In a few generations, the salmon will be only a
portrait in a book.

and traded their salmon
for a soft dollar
until one of the
Cannery Row pioneers
figured a dead fish
is a stinking fish
unless you can can it.
He built a cannery
and bought the salmon:
but he had his eye on the future.
When he looked at his records
in 1904 he said:
"Now let's see!
If I'm canning 28 tons a day,
that makes 840 tons of salmon a month . . .
that's a helluva lot of salmon,
and a lot of folks are eating it fresh—
a helluva lot of it fresh—
and a helluva lot and a helluva lot
makes one helluva lot."

Meanwhile the salmon
exhausted themselves
trying to make love faster
to keep up with demand.

Man glorified the eagle in legend, in song, on coin,
then shot them out of the sky for sport, and appeased
his conscience by stuffing a few.

SOME MEN need to rest in an eagle's nest
and roar with the strength of a lion,
sit on the top of the tallest tree
on top of the tallest mountain
and nurture a dream
that is more than a dream;
to capture the cave
of the mountain king,
call the unknown by name—
strike it rich!
They grabbed an eagle in flight
and melted him into American coin.

These men had a dream;
    to be the first pioneer,
    "thinker-upper for the first time."
They burned with passion
    to be "advance" men for a new era.
But it's hard to talk

A thread of life ties all things together, tiger and chick, goat and sardine. The overkill of one, one day, will be felt by all.

to running men,
hurried along by a silver eagle
in each hand.

The winds of "progress"
drown out
the quiet moan of famine.

"What's a little famine
so long as you're eating good?"
say the advertising copy writers
on Madison Avenue.

Don't blame the canner,
digger-of-truffles,
lobster-netter,
elk-hunter,
eel-pickler,
sparrow-smoker.
The whole world is a big "eat-me-up."

(We'll eat the song of sparrows
in the morning.)

Some guy in a New York bar said:
"I'm like a dog. If I can't eat it
or screw it, piss on it."
"That's a good one,"
his friend said in
Chicago, Florida, Oshkosh, and Cannery Row.
One corporation giant
jotted it down in his note book:

We bomb our foods with deadly poison and sicken the mother's milk. The lethal chemicals end up in the sea, turning fish into carriers of death.

"I'll pass it along to my advertising agency,
    maybe they can clean it up a little."

"The big thing
    is how to catch sardines," the canner said.

Big thing is how to:
    mine more iron,
    sponge up mercury,
    use thin pine for toothpicks,
    kill seal for fur coats;
    bomb the earth with poison,
    kill everything that threatens a profit,
    man, beast, and insect!
Where does profit stop
    and sanity begin?

"They got their production problems
    and I had mine," the canner said.
"I want you to know the 'tormendous'
    handicaps we overcome.
If you're 'inerested' in the truth,
    you come to the right party,
    but if you want to talk about
    eel-picklers and pine-tree toothpicks
    and all the rest of that crap
    we can call it quits right now.
I'm a good American and I don't like
    to hear nobody running down
    American business, because
    America is business
    and America means business
    and don't you ever forget it.

After the sardines were fished out, many lampara nets were cut up and sold to tourists. A few lampara nets are still at work fishing anchovies out of the bay— for fertilizer.

It was good American know-how
    that *built* the fishing business.
You can't imagine the sweat that built Cannery Row.
It didn't just grow like a weed.
It took work and good money.
Cost lives
    with them damn fool fishermen
    taking all kinds of chances.
That was the old spirit:
    'blood, guts, and tears' like George Washington
    or somebody said.
It was no accident when we
    came up with the answer.
We thought it out, mulled it over,
    talked about it,
    then it come in a flash:
    when you look to Jesus for the answer,
    he'll lay it in your hand.
There was this old wop fisherman
    from Sicily who said:
    'If it's good enough for Christ,
    it's good enough for us.'
He didn't say it just that way.
You know how wops talk.
So I said, 'What in hell you talking about?' "

—Lampara net. They been using
    it in the old country before Jesus—

"So we ordered one of them
    lampara nets from the old country.
If you saw it, you'd damn well know

81

Crabs and shellfish have met the same fate as the sardine.
Many areas once famous for crabs now import frozen
crabs from other waters. How long before they, too,
will be fished out?

what I'm talking about.
That net is so fine wove
   it can't miss
   a fish's fart.
All the wops were smart.
There's this smart old
   wop just in from the old country
   and he got himself a job
   pulling crabs out of nets
   on a crab boat.
First week his fingers looked
   like chopped meat from all the bites.
So he took to chewing tobacco
   and everytime one of them crabs
   latched on to his finger,
   he spit a wad of
   tobacco juice in the crab's eye
   and that crab opened his pinchers
   faster than the gals opened
   their legs
   in Flora's whorehouse.
That's back in
   the good old days when there was
   lots of crabs around.
Don't know where in hell
   they got to, but they
   sure disappeared.
Getting back to the lampara net,
   it was the best thing
   that came out of
   Christ's backyard.
You could almost scoop up

.etch from "High . L.

The following figures represent the tons each individual seiner in the Monterey Sardine 1 season. Each figure is accurate, but in a few case mate due to small late catches. The boats represent. ed from 90 tons to 200 tons, except for the three labe ing they are "baby seiners" with about 35 tons cape icity.

ered by
1945-46
be approxi-
save capacities
led "B," indicat-

August 1, 1945 to January 31, 1946

NAME OF BOATS	TONNAGE
1. Liberator	4297.41
New Marettimo	4841.28
3. Diana	4032.59
4. Dian A	3962.74
5. Aurora	3760.24
6. Sea Traveler	3620.97
7. Lina V	3242.05
8. Lina V II	3059.74
9. J. D. Martinolic	3023.37
10. Sea Boy	2773.92
11. Vagabond	2762.06
12. Paolina T	2706.55
13. American Rose	2636.98
14. Mineo Brothers	2596.80
15. Star of Monterey	2583.07
16. New of Monterey	2540.49
18. Endeavoroma	2515.40
19. Pacific St	2477.61
20. Sea Queen T	2462.98
21. A. Ferrante	2389.63
22. Lorraine A	2357.74
23. Janita	2347.27
24. Eastern Star	2235.04
25. California Rose	2139.23
26. San Vito	2112.06
27. Tonic	2091.73
28. Sea Maid	2069.99
29. Santa Rita	2039.14
30. Flaminian	2030.85

Official record of the seiners' catch in 1946: many of the boats carried payloads of 200 tons. Today they drag the California coast, or deplete the fish in foreign waters.

the whole bay with one net.
Easy to use, too.
One boat took one end
    and another boat took the other end
    and made a big circle around
    a school of sardines and
    Wham!
    They pulled a rope and the net
    closed in on a big bag of money."

The lampara net,
    a contribution
    from time before Christ,
    was improved upon,
    modified,
    altered,
    made bigger,
    woven tighter,
    weighted heavier,
    dropped deeper,
    built stronger—
    and even Christ
    would have been impressed
    with American know-how.

There's this cab driver
    who used to be a sardine
    fisherman and now he sells
    nostalgia for a tip.
After he sings a verse or two
    from his favorite song,
    like:

Diana, one of the finest seiners afloat. When the sardines were gone, she regeared. Today she drags the bottom of the ocean for anything she can scoop up in her net.

"How did they bury Flora Wood,
They buried her in the sand,
She had a Bible on her chest
And two bucks in her hand . . ."
he lapses into
a soliloquy about the days
when he "murdered" the fish:
"We'd pull up the nets,
tighten the net collar and them
sardines was practically canned
before we pulled them out
of the water and if we had
too much, we'd just let the
rest of 'em float dead for the seagulls."

"The lampara net," says
the City of Monterey
in a little book
you can get for free:
"Completely revolutionized
commercial fishing in California
and represented the first stage
in the evolution of sardine
seining operations
in Monterey Bay.
It was now possible
for boats to bring in
unheard of catches
weighing 25 to 30 tons."
Thirty tons and 30 tons
make 60 tons
and 60 tons and 60 tons

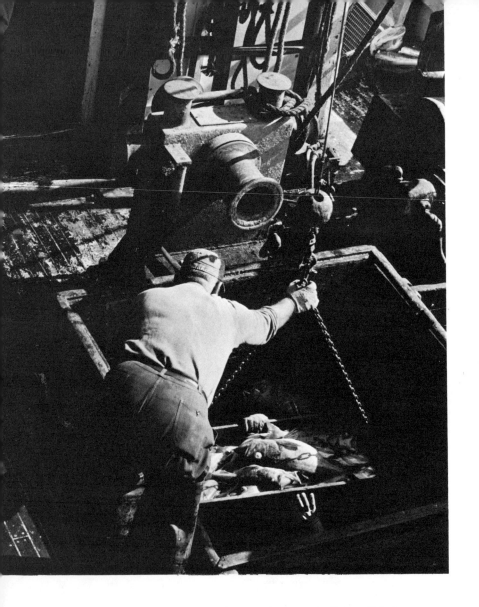

All nations must join together and protect all the fish in
all the waters of the world. Or well-oiled iron and escape-
proof nets will empty the well that feeds our hunger.

make 120 tons
and 120 tons and . . .

Fishermen
    improved their gear,
    built bigger boats for bigger nets,
    bigger nets for bigger boats,
    faster engines
    to cover the bay,
    well oiled iron
    to hoist the fish
    and dump them into the fat belly
    of fishing boats
    that were getting fatter all the time.

The indomitable spirit
    and marching feet
    of the pioneer
    and advance man
    prevails over all:
    marching to variations
    on a theme by "progress."
Sometimes "progress"
    is a breech cloth
    for a healthy staff of greed
    hiding underneath,
    although there's little
    question that society
    wouldn't have reached this
    high degree of economic
    and moral "integrity"
    without a constant prodding.

When the small fish were gone, man made stronger nets
of bigger mesh to hold the larger fish.

Every "progress" brings a new problem,
   each new problem brings a "progress":
   fisherman prodded the canner,
   canner prodded the fisherman.
When the boats were too small,
   the cannery was too big.
When the cannery was too big,
   the boats were too small.

If the foundry's too small
   to smelt the ore,
   mill's too small
   to cut the timber,
   refinery's too small
   to make the oil,
   guns too small
   to kill the "enemy,"
   and the cannery's too small
   to can the fish,
   there's a prod
   from under the breech cloth
   that makes a man
   build them bigger.

Rustle of silver-eagle wings!

"Big" is as big as the entire earth,
   as infinite as space.
And small?
A man would have to search forever
   and then he would find only
   a place to begin.

Iron doors and heavy weights hold the drag net close to
the ocean floor, scraping up every variety of fish in its path,
including the fish eggs of future generations.

"Ya wanna know 'big'?
I'll tell ya big,"
   the old fisherman said.
"The New Marettimo.
She was big.
Carried a hundred and fifty ton of fish."
"Go on, Sal," the canner said.
"You're barkin' up my ass.
Marettimo couldn't reach
   Sea Boy's belly.
Talkin' about big, you should have
   seen Sea Boy . . ."

Perhaps a boat as long as the ocean is long,
   wide as the ocean is wide,
   deep as the ocean is deep.
Would that be "big enough"?
"You forgot one thing," the canner said.
"You gotta leave room
   to get the fish out."

The old fisherman shook his head:
"If we left it to them canners,
   they'd put a pump in
   the ocean and drain
   out the water."
"We had to get bigger.
That's the nature of business,"
   the canner said.
"Any smart businessman'll tell you.
If you don't get in there and
   get big first,

With the crabs gone and the salmon getting scarce, small
fishermen can barely pay the overhead on their boats.

some shark'll swallow you up.
Lot healthier being the shark.
Sal'll tell you,
    there was a time we was so jammed up
    in the cannery
    the fish got to stinking
    while they was waiting
    out there in the bay.
Cannery was too small.
So I made it bigger
    to take care of Sal
    and the rest of the fishermen.
Ain't that right, Sal?"
"Stop the crap," Sal said.
"Times you made us sit out there
    with them fresh fish
    hoping they'd raise a little stink
    so we'd get scared to death
    and drop our prices.
That wasn't good enough
    so you short-weighted us, too. . . .
I know. I heard the story a million times.
Now you're going to tell me
    how much money you gave the church."

"Let's face it," the canner said,
    "if it wasn't for the canners
    pushing the fishermen,
    where would you be today?"
"Maybe fishing," Sal said.

"If you want the facts," the canner said,

Most of us live only by the fruit of honest labor, like
this old lady who spent her best years working in a fish
cannery. The poor are the first to suffer from the brutal
hunger of hollow men.

"catching fish is only one side
of the story.
Getting the damn things
to lay down nice and pretty in a can,
that's what took the real
brain dance.
When this fishing thing
broke loose on Cannery Row
it was a knock-me-down, drag-me-out
fight with all kinds of problems.
You can imagine
with all them fish swimming around
out there and
us cutting them,
cleaning them,
cooking them,
dragging them through boiling oil,
putting them in a can. . . .
All by hand!
It would take forever to can them all.
Who in hell can live that long?
So we installed
all this automatic stuff
to make the work easier,
and all the women did was complain
they wasn't getting enough work
and they was underpaid.
If that ain't like women for you.
Here we go to all that expense
putting in
cleaners,
cutters,

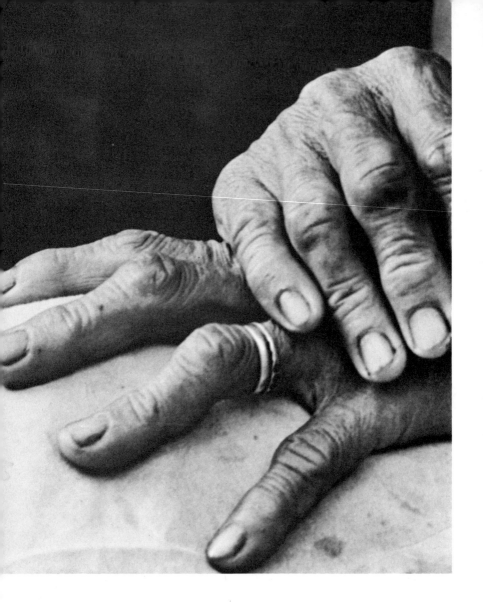

"I don't mind none that my hands hurt from the days I worked in the cannery. It fed my children and helped me raise a good family . . ."

cookers,
boilers,
conveyors,
belt lifts,
lots of windows for fresh air.
A Lady's room, too.
You can say
  from beginning to end
  Cannery Row is a
  success story.
What they're doin' in Detroit
  we did on Cannery Row.
Talk about production,
  I can tell you all about
  production.
We shot them cans of sardines
  off that assembly line
  like machine gun bullets.
Wasn't a slacker among us
  from the beginning
  right up to the time we closed down.
Listen to these figures,
  numbers don't lie:
  1900: 400 *cans* of sardines.
  1912: seventy thousand *cases.*
  1918: one million, four hundred thousand *cases.*

War helped a little in '18.
Moved a lot of fish.
I ain't a war-lover," the canner said.
"Don't believe in all that killing
Unless it's needed.

Relics of a better year: rusting shovel and canning salt.

But when they signed that armistice
   in '18
   it was like signing
   our bankrupt papers.
Before the war we was getting
   two dollars and fourteen cents
   a case.
During the war
   the government paid us
   seven dollars and fifty cents
   a case.

When Johnny come marching
   home again,
   we couldn't sell
   canned sardines for beans."
The canner shook his head
   in recollection
   of better days.

War in the name of
   peace and freedom,
   war in the name of God
   and country,
   war in the name
   of the founding fathers . . .
   good for the economy,
   made jobs,
   made profit,
   made orphans;
   sold sardines,
   fed the troops.

This cannery is no more. The land has been cleared for a tourist complex. But its machinery is alive and kicking out cans of fish on coastal waters of other lands.

Easy to handle,
    easy to can,
    easy to ship.
Stick them down your throat,
    stuff them in your ear,
    use them for toilet paper,
    but "for Christ's sake
    move sardines."

By the time
    it was all over
    "over there,"
    seven billion pounds of fish
    were hauled out
    of Monterey bay,
    ". . . and there was lots more left."
Scratch of the armistice pen
    was a loud squeak
    in the "wheels of progress."
"When I fired my crews after
    the first World War, I told them,
    'Dont worry one damn bit.
Stick around Cannery Row.
We'll come up with the answer.'"

      The truth if its out
      Resounds with a clatter,
      If progress stands still,
      There's something the matter.
      There's fish in the ocean
      And ore in the earth,
      Trees to cut down,

There was a demand for cheap chicken feed, so the reduction plants turned out chicken feed and exported it to other nations.

Regardless of girth.
The "leader" of man
With snoot of a beagle,
Points straight to the nest
Of the "silver eagle."

There's more to do with a tree
    than build a house,
    more to do with coal
    than burn it,
    more to do with oil
    than run a machine,
    more to do with corn
    than feed a cow,
    more to do with sardines
    than put them in cans.

"That's the heart of progress,"
    the canner said, "finding out
    something to do with something
    that you were doing
    something else with before."

And there were lots of things to do with sardines:
    you could turn them into
    chicken feed,
    fertilizer,
    paint,
    fish oil,
    fish-meal,
    explosives,
    and besides that was a lot

"It was a crime against God and man the way they killed off the sardines. When I worked in the cannery, they destroyed millions of fish eggs. Just swept them into the reducer . . ."

cheaper than canning the fish
and it made more profit.
"So we went to Sacramento
and talked to the men who made the laws.
We explained that if
they woudn't let us
'reduce' the fish
the canning industry would
be 'reduced' to a pauper.
They were smart guys,
they knew people come before fish.
They also knew a word and a buck
from the canners
could cook their goose
next election.
So the politicians said
'Okay, reduce the damn fish.'

That was the beginning of great times
on the row, wasn't it, Joe?
Go on and tell him.
You been around here from the beginning."

"I'm 92," Joe said,
eyes surprised
like he heard his age
for the first time.
His words were quiet
like Monterey fog.
He was thin as a trolling spar,
arms hung taut
as trolling lines,

One giant American canning firm sends prospectors around the world. Last "strike" was in the Persian gulf. Derricks and drag nets are on the way to clean out the fish.

with a leaden weight
of wasted years
in each hand.
Harsh winds, burning sun
and smoldering dreams
charred his face.
But his fingers were still nimble
for mending nets.
"I go down to the bay every day
to make sure the boats are still there."
The canner tapped his forehead:
"Joe was one of my best fishermen,"
he said, tapping his head again.
"Lost his son in the war.
Been a little off ever since.
Sometimes he sits down there on the dock
and talks to a seagull."
"Sometimes I talk to a seagull," Joe said.

Some people have a quaint way
of justifying dishonor, lies and plunder,
with a trite twist of a phrase.
A major tragedy
can be "reduced" to nothing,
like the sardines
after the meat,
skin and bones
came out of the crusher
and the stink was wafted away
on a Monterey breeze.
"Guess we closed the barn door
after the cow got out,"

The fish are gone. The crematory remains.

the lawmakers said.
After the sardines were
    canned,
    crushed,
    pulverized,
    and all eaten up
    by man, chicken,
    and a paint company.

Laws are written by a lobby
    with the quill of the "silver eagle":
Section 1070 of the 1939
    California Fish and Game code said:
        "Persons engaged in preserving sardines:
        ... may use in a reduction plant
        or by reduction process
        such sardines or fish
        delivered mixed with sardines,
        unfit for drying, salting,
        smoking, or pickling ..."

"Back in the old days I was
    a packer,"
an old Mexican woman said.
"Even my daughters worked in the
    canneries.
It was crazy what happened.
One day there was no more fish. . . ."

The oldest daughter said:
    "You wouldn't believe it.
They dumped all the good fish
    in the cannery
    and, instead of canning them,

they squashed them up for oil
or fertilizer."

"I asked the foreman,
     I said, these are good fish.
Why do you reduce them?"
     the mother said.

"We needed our jobs," the
     youngest daughter said. "We got
     twenty-five cents an hour. If
     they reduced all the fish,
     we wouldn't have any work to do."

"They wasn't supposed to
     reduce good fish," the oldest
     daughter said. "But the foreman
     said he'd fire us if we didn't
     keep our mouth shut."

"It was like a curse,"
     the mother said, crossing herself.
"Overnight it was like a cemetery."

Seven years later
     the lights went out on Glory row.
There was nothing left to can
     but squid.
Cut it, dice, it, stretch it,
     dress it in tomato sauce,
     label it "great"—it was still squid,
     (and even they were getting fewer).

113

All the smoke stacks are cold, now. Tombstones to a planless pillage of the sea.

In 1946 the wise men
   from Sacramento
   made a pilgrimage to Monterey . . .
They took a voyage around the bay
   to size up the situation.

"Reduction is criminal," the first lawmaker said.

"We'll pass a law
   against it," the second lawmaker said.

"There isn't one silly
   sardine left in the bay," the third lawmaker said.

The fourth lawmaker clapped
   his hands and screamed in
   orgasmic pleasure;
   "The hell there isn't.
I just saw an old sardine
   chasing another one. He must
   be courtin'."

That made the lawmakers
   boisterously happy:
"Our pilgrimage is not in vain,"
   they said in unison. "We'll pass
   a law, we'll pass a law.
Reduction is a crime!
We'll let the two sardines
   make a comeback."
The lawmakers felt a quiet joy
   in their hearts.

Equipment from this cannery was sent to Peru and helped devastate the fish population in that South American country.

They solved a problem
and saved two romantic sardines.

Arm in arm
   they walked down Cannery Row singing:
     "We passed a law,
     We saved the fish,
     No one can deny.
     All the canners have to do
     Is let them multiply.
     We passed a law,
     We saved the fish,
     We've spared the canners' tears.
     His business will bloom again
      in twenty thousand years.
     In twenty thousand years, yo ho,
     In twenty thousand years."
Suddenly the first lawmaker stopped singing:
   "Somebody'll nail us sure as hell," he said.
"We're the guys
   who okayed reduction in the first place."

"Don't sweat it," the second
   lawmaker said,
"The canners and fishermen
   will back us.
Nobody wants to be wrong.
Listen to this:
'Hey, Mario, what happened to the fish?'
—'The big squids ate up all the little sardines'—

 'Hey, Seppi, where did the fish go?'
  —'Water got too cold'—

Cannery and reduction equipment from Cannery Row, Monterey, along with new, improved devices, are now emptying the waters around Japan.

'Hey, Sven, why did the fish go away?'
—'Currents changed'—

'Hey, Vince, who killed all the fish?'
—'Army dumped poison in the bay'—

"See," the second lawmaker said.
"We got our alibi. They'll testify
   to where we were on the night of
   the 'reduction.' "

And they all sang another chorus
   of their song:
      "We passed a law,
      We saved the fishes,
      Two schnitzels, two pretzels,
      Two fertile knishes.
      The laws of copulation
      Are the same in every nation. . . .
      It only takes a 'pair' to save the day!
      And now with our arrival
      You can brush away your fears.
      We guarantee survival
      . . . in twenty thousand years."

The fishermen and canners
   didn't take kindly
   to the entertainment,
   denying they sent
   the lobby that bought
   the "reduction law"
   in the first place.

Forests were devastated to build canneries like this. Now there is a shortage of lumber—and the fish are gone too.

Canneries closed down,
   small fishermen
   and cannery workers
   went hungry.
   Fishermen sold
   their seiners
   to other fishermen
   in other ports,
   and the hungry lampara net
   from Christ's hometown
   went to eating again
   in other waters.

Cannery Row
   became a ghost street
   where sardine souls
   rode on the ghost-back
   of the condor
   and huddled by invisible camp fires
   of long dead red men
   and talked to the
   bison souls
   about the white man's dream.

The body of a living thing
is tied to every part
of the universe,
trees, birds, fish, mammals.
When man depletes
   the fish, a part of every
   living thing dies a little.
When man depletes the forests,
   each living thing dies a little more.

121

We steal from the earth, rob the sea, and try to dispose
of the evidence by tossing the slop on the water. No
tide is strong enough to carry away the proof of our
plunder.

How much dying can there be
  before there is
  total death?

Still man ploughs the earth sterile,
  and dreams his plastic dreams:
  to buy a thing
  and win a bet,
  trade a car,
  build an empire,
  buy a suit
  with two pairs of pants,
  hoard silver dollars
  and bury gold in his basement.
He
  rents a warehouse
  and stockpiles lumber,
  rice,
  wheat,
  corn,
  cotton,
  eggs,
  beef,
  iron,
  rubber,
  fish;
  stockpiles against the day
  when stockpiling
  makes shortages
  and drives the prices up.
He
  corners the market

123

Man generates power to make more power. Unregulated, unplanned, heedless of the consequences, he gets the most out of today and kills tomorrow.

on canned tomatoes,
string beans
and anal salve.
He buries himself in "things"
and gives "meaning" to his empty days
with high-priced call girls
and turns his liver green with booze.
He mines the mine
while the mining is good,
salts it down when the mine runs dry
and sells it to a "sucker."
He
puts sawdust
in the auto transmission
and peddles it to a child.
He
Bible-paints his brain
and sells it to God
on Sunday morning.

Who is to say man has
a lesser dream than God?
That Cannery Row is
a street other than yours?
The silence on
Cannery Row
is contagious;
it moves among all men
in all places.
The dead are silent
and the living are afraid to talk
—for fear they'll spoil a profit.

A cannery door that goes nowhere!

Cannery Row,
   a desolate street of
   decaying barns,
   of long dead wood,
   rusting iron,
   rotting floors and rafters,
   sagging roofs and leaning walls,
   filling the appetites
   of wind and rain,
   termites and vandals.
The fisherfolk were seventh.

But Seventh is never last.

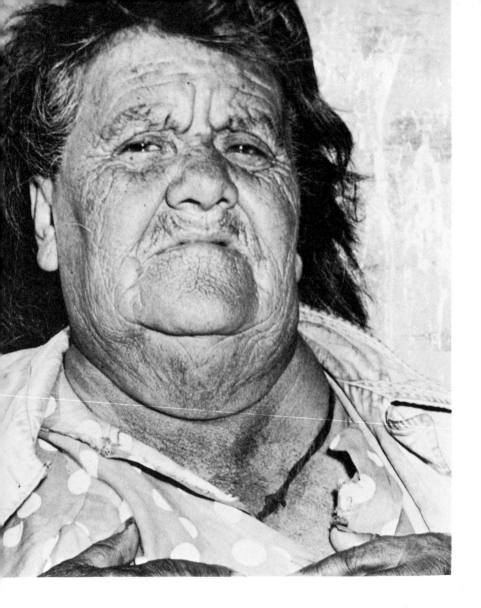

"So I was a streetwalker.
I didn't hurt nobody . . ."

CANNERY ROW
     became a campground
     for another tribe
of lost pedestrians
who moved like fog shadows
into vacant buildings
and called the barns
home:
Wino and cast-out,
pimp and con-man,
derelict and fugitive,
dreamer and poet.
They slept under the canneries,
    cooked their food over
    canned heat,
    strained the canned heat
    through dirty socks
    and drank the alcohol,

Over the mast of a model ship and across the street is
Doc Ricketts' lab. It's a private "keyclub," now, where
a select group of gentlemen toast the "glory" of old
Cannery Row.

made their homes in rusting pipes,
pimped for the rent-paying whorehouses
and pan-handled the babbit,
fisherman, canner
and politician
who slipped away from their wives
for an hour in bed
with a one-dollar whore.

Bertha walked from Salinas
   to Cannery Row,
   bringing only the tools
   she got from God,
   soft and fresh
   as newly cooked farm bread,
   young as the first shoot
   of an Iowa corn stalk,
   clean-smelling
   as the morning winds
   from the meadow.
"When I got to Cannery Row,
   all I had was a dollar and
   some change and a letter
   of 'interduction' to Flora Wood.
She gave me a job.
Guess I should've knowed better
   but I wasn't 'edjacated'
   till lately," Bertha said
   in her
   San Francisco
   slum flat many years later.
"Flora was good to us girls,

treated us better than a mother.
Put mustard plaster on our chests
    when we had a cold and gave us
    hot tea.
Flora was a God-fearing woman."
Bertha brushed away a wisp
    of gray hair from her pouchy eyes
    with the hand that held her Rosary.
"They wasn't just bums
    on Cannery Row,
    they was lonely, scared men
    who hid like bugs in whores' beds.
Men who fished
    and cleaned the fish,
    canned the fish
    and cooked the fish
    and when I loved them at night,
    they stank of fish.
But the smell was a God-smell
    and I come to love the fishermen
    and the cannery workers.
And them you call bums.
I laid down with lots of the
    better known gentlemen, too.
When they seen me on the street,
    they made remarks
    about what I was,
    God help them.
Guess them that can,
    get finer women now.
In my day, they said
    we was wicked women.

"And the seagull was always eating slop."

Now the fresh young things
    do it right in living daylight
    where you can throw them
    a dime for the show.
I can never forget that
    old Cannery Row
    with the stink of fish guts on the beach
    and them flies!
And the seagulls always eating slop.
And the cannery whistles
    when the fish was in.
It was more full of
    goodness than I ever knowed before.
Never could figger just how come
    the street just laid down and died.
There was one fisherman
    who come to me to love
    but he just sat him on the
    side of the bed
    and cried like he was fit
    for his mother to take
    in her arms.
He was broke and couldn't
    catch any fish and he was
    having to sell his boat.
So he asked me to pray to God
    to bring back the fish
    when I go to the church with
    Flora on Sunday.
From what I hear
    there was more good love
    on Cannery Row when it was

Cannery Row, Monterey. Japan? Sweden? Portugal? Spain? Italy? Philippines? "Sure it could happen. But not likely in 'our' generation," a canner said in Germany.

full of working people
than it is now
with all them spangles
and glitter.
I don't have much smarts
but I got a good smeller
and I smelled a long time ago
after Flora died that the world
was going to hell.
We was a clean bunch of girls
back then, with the ol' doc
looking us over every now and then.
Now you got all them fine people
who calls themselves clean today
and they're messin' up the world
till a soul could die of the stink.
I read a book about
Cannery Row
that a fellow named
'Steinbecker' wrote.
He sure hit the nail
on the head.
Lots of them folks was heroes.
To my way of thinking,
all them heroes is dead now.
Most of the men are whores.
Worse to sell your soul
for a dollar
than your body.
I'm a Catholic now
and Christ
will forgive my sins.

Last vestiges of Cannery Row, Monterey . . .
"It is our success that is destroying us . . ."

But he never did give
    them money lenders the time of day. . . ."

Without knowing
    or wanting to,
    better than
    Madison Avenue advertising hacks,
    better than fast talking
    press agents,
    better than high-pressure
    land peddlers,
    better than a Chamber of Commerce,
    Steinbeck made Cannery Row
    one of the best known streets
    in the world.
Yet he would be the first to say
    that wherever man works
    and drains the ocean or the earth,
    there is a Cannery Row.
And he would be the first to say:
"We have succeeded in what
    our fathers prayed for
    and it is our success
    that is destroying us. . . ."
The Steinbeck story came eighth.

But Eighth is never last.

The fruit stand is closed, the land is up for sale, the trees are being rooted out and this is the last crop of fruit from another orchard.

ENTER the economic seer,
man of all ventures,
wise in finance,
student of population trends,
alert to land values,
purveyor of "progress,"
procurer for profit.

With feet spread apart,
hands on hips,
he looks over the land,
any land, all land:
fruit orchards that shower
flower petals
on interstate highways,
fields of wheat
suffocating in fumes
of diesel fuel,
acres of meadows

Every piece of equipment that could be used again was shipped to another place for another cannery. Everything was salvaged but the fish.

that have no need
of being something else,
coasts of oceans
and shores of rivers.
"This is going to take
some looking into," the
land developer says,
"but with the help of my
computer, we'll sure as hell
come up with the
highest and best economic use.'"

"The fish are dead and gone,
      God rest their souls in olive oil,"
      says the seer.
"But we still have the land
      where the canneries canned them.
We can still sell, trade
      and convert the land
      where the canneries stand.
All that equipment
      is worth a fortune.
All we have to do is
      find a buyer."

The seer
      walked up and down Cannery Row,
      studied the old barns,
      examined the rusting equipment,
      weighed out the metal
      on his scale of experience
      and concluded that:

There are more fish in other lands and with modern know-how, who knows how long it will take to wipe them out?

"This street is a good investment.
"It'll make
   a dozen millionaires."
He bought the canneries
   for the "junk" in them and
   got the barn and the land it
   stood on "for a song."
He knew the cannery equipment alone
   was worth a fortune.
He put the land on ice
   and milked the "junk."
Fish were gone from Monterey bay
   but the seer knew
   there were more fish in
   other bays
   ripe for harvesting,
   canning,
   reducing,
   pressing,
   crushing and drying.
"Would be a sin
   to let this equipment
   go to waste," the seer said.
He cannibalized the canneries,
   sold the conveyors,
   boilers, belts, crushers,
   motors and fittings
   to fishing villages
   all over the world.

A former cannery owner
   said: "There's a helluva story

145

There were about 20 fish-processing plants on Cannery
Row, give or take a few for arson.

on this street. Just figure it,
there's 425 tons of metal in
every cannery and there were
18 canneries and two reduction plants,
give or take one or two for arson.
That's a lot of machinery,
and the great thing about it is,
it's not going to waste.
Every last screw and nut
will be working somewhere else
in the world."

All shipped COD
and with best wishes
for a profitable yield
from Cannery Row, Monterey
to Cannery Row,
Mexico, Peru,
South Africa,
Puerto Rico,
Venezuela,
Japan,
the Philippines,
Australia,
New Zealand, and Canada.

By the way, how many
bays are there in the world?
What's the census of fish?
The seer didn't know,
the canner didn't know,
the fisherman didn't know,

Some of the ground was cleared for new commercial buildings. A few were renovated to house the "new pioneers."

and *nobody really gave a damn*—
so long as their investment dollar
was "yielding the highest
possible return."

"Time to get on with 'progress,' "
   the seer said. "Can't afford to
   sit on these canneries:
   reinforce the roofs!
   support the walls!
   brace the floors!
   divide them!
   subdivide them!
Paint in the termites,
   paint out the rain.
Put out a sign:
   'Space for Rent'
   on sixty-eight acres
   of beautiful Monterey coast,
   California's new Riviera."

The land rush was on.
The new pioneers were
   candlemakers,
   dealers in tea
   and herbs,
   sex tonics
   and body oils,
   hash pipes
   and cigarette papers,
   wines and liquors
   and Japanese porcelain.

149

Cannery Row . . . new grotesques of wood and noise
and carnival lights.

Hawkers of
   food and rags,
   leather chastity belts
   and aluminum brassieres.
Art by tomorrow's masters
   and masters of the con arts.
Boutiques,
   discotheques,
   antiques,
   salesmen's samples,
   and rusting relics
   of the fishing fleet.

Gone the condor
   and bison,
   gone is ancient man
   and the Indian he fathered.
Gone the Spaniard
   and the first pioneer,
   gone the Italian
   and Portuguese fishermen,
   gone the wino and whore. . . .

Fading shadows
   in the evening fog,
   replaced by hucksters
   and new grotesques
   of wood and noise
   and carnival lights.

But Last is never last.

EPILOGUE

WHEN the scent of flowers
        have been vacuum packed
        as mementos
of a better day
and there is no one left
to open a can and recall
the dream of a summer's night;
when rusting bank vaults
hold a crop of overripe dollars
and there is no one left to
harvest the seedless fruit,
when the sky has been plucked of birds
and the last fish dragged
from the ocean bottom,
who will be left to scream:
"panic-crier,
doomsday prophet,
courier of evil tidings"?

Just as man is depleting the oceans, the land, and the forests, so he is depleting the animals. One day the leather tannery, too, will be an empty barn.

The history of man
   is a record of
   "closing the barn door
   after the cow gets out."
Or saying it the way
   one promoter said it:
   "Who gives a shit
   what happens
   a thousand years from now,
   I'm getting my profit
   while the getting is good.
When I die,
   I'll be cremated.
Nobody's going to
   piss on my grave. . . ."

The land developer,
   merchandiser,
   food-converter,
   sea-strainer,
   lake-drainer,
   mountain-mover,
   leather-tanner,
   orchard-killer,
   forest-stripper,
   earth-reducer,
   equate the world with "capital return."
Each venture must be
   considered,
   reconsidered,
   weighed,
   computerized,

Youth is tired of being trespassers on an earth that belongs to them.

figured against costs,
   capitalized,
   and amortized.
Any textbook on economics
   will explain that every
   business venture must be
   economically feasible
   and to the best interest
   of the investor,
   guaranteeing a sound return
   on the investment dollar.

If land makes more profit
   than wheat,
   tear out the wheat;
   if land makes more profit
   than apples,
   tear out the apple tree.
How many dead orchards
   and grain fields,
   vineyards
   and sorgum farms,
   lettuce fields,
   and orange groves
   lie under the tombstones
   of shopping centers?
How long before the fruit stall
   on top of a buried orchard
   is empty of fruit?
Not long!

But there is time. . . .

Mankind mourns for Christ, but defames Christ's dream by crucifying the earth and all of its creatures.

"Keep faith," a father said to his child.
"Keep faith with our founding fathers,
    gentlemen of sly humor
    with their eye on an honest profit.
Keep faith with your ancestors,
    pioneers who built mansions
    in a wilderness
    and ships to conquer the oceans.
Look to history for your 'heroes'
    and forgive our politicians
    their trespasses
    for they are only human
    and every man has a little
    greed and larceny in his heart.
It's just that you're a little young now.
You'll mellow with age,
    you'll forget your idealism.
And when you're older,
    you'll laugh at the romantic garbage
    of your youth
    while you're spending dividends
    from blue chip stocks
    that papa salted away for you."

"Faith?" asked his child.
"Your god is a golden lamb.
Your 'heroes' stoop
    with the heavy weight of medals
    in memory of massive killings.
Your leaders churn milk
    into dividends,
    crush fish into explosives;

159

your promises are as brittle
as the Bill of Rights on charred parchment.
Your leaders took from the land
and gave to the bank,
taxed the poor and gave to the rich,
soiled my lungs with noxious gas
and made my body sick with poison
on a wax-polished apple.
Your leaders and heroes
have stolen the food
from the mouths of my unborn children.
Keep your vows of packaged love!
Look through
the worm holes in your deeds of 'owning'
and see the ocean and mountain
on the other side."

I walked a forest path
and tore my arm
on a barbed wire fence.
Is love a deed of trust
on acres of fenced land
that no one really owns?

Bury your heroes
and leaders
in the text
of your deceptive history.

We will read new books, now.
We must have a better dream than our fathers!

While man stumbles beneath the weight
    of shabby dreams,
    childhood still finds joy
    on a soiled earth.
They *must* make it clean again!

Precious youth,
be deaf to the croaking
of old frogs!

Photo by Dave Allen

Tom Weber, native of New York's "hell's kitchen," has been a photo-journalist since he was 18 years old. His work includes: reporter, editor, and photographer on metropolitan newspapers and magazines. He has also been a stevedore on the San Francisco waterfront and a commercial fisherman.

Weber has been around the world four times, making pictures of people in every major nation. He has been taking pictures of *Cannery Row* for 25 years. For the last 12 years his studio has been the loft of an old cannery on *Cannery Row.* He lives in Monterey, California, with his wife and large family.